MESSAGES
FROM THE
Unicorns
COLOURING BOOK

MESSAGES
FROM THE
Unicorns
COLOURING BOOK

DOREEN VIRTUE

Illustrations by Heather Luciana

HAY HOUSE

Carlsbad, California • New York City • London
Sydney • Johannesburg • Vancouver • New Delhi

First published and distributed in the United Kingdom by:
Hay House UK Ltd, Astley House, 33 Notting Hill Gate, London W11 3JQ
Tel: +44 (0)20 3675 2450; Fax: +44 (0)20 3675 2451; www.hayhouse.co.uk

Published and distributed in the United States of America by:
Hay House Inc., PO Box 5100, Carlsbad, CA 92018-5100
Tel: (1) 760 431 7695 or (800) 654 5126
Fax: (1) 760 431 6948 or (800) 650 5115; www.hayhouse.com

Published and distributed in Australia by:
Hay House Australia Ltd, 18/36 Ralph St, Alexandria NSW 2015
Tel: (61) 2 9669 4299; Fax: (61) 2 9669 4144; www.hayhouse.com.au

Published and distributed in the Republic of South Africa by:
Hay House SA (Pty) Ltd, PO Box 990, Witkoppen 2068
info@hayhouse.co.za; www.hayhouse.co.za

Published and distributed in India by:
Hay House Publishers India, Muskaan Complex, Plot No.3, B-2,
Vasant Kunj, New Delhi 110 070
Tel: (91) 11 4176 1620; Fax: (91) 11 4176 1630; www.hayhouse.co.in

Distributed in Canada by:
Raincoast Books, 2440 Viking Way, Richmond, B.C. V6V 1N2
Tel: (1) 604 448 7100; Fax: (1) 604 270 7161; www.raincoast.com

A catalogue record for this book is available from the British Library.

ISBN: 978-1-78180-815-3

Printed and bound by CPI Group (UK) Ltd, Croydon, CR0 4YY

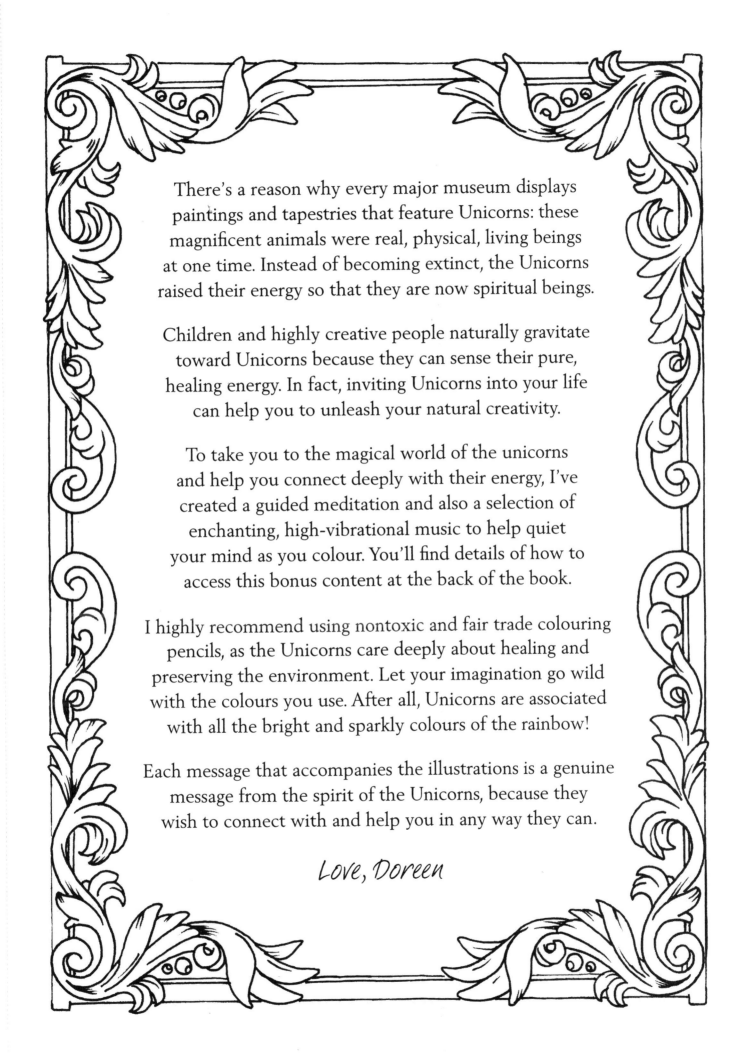

There's a reason why every major museum displays paintings and tapestries that feature Unicorns: these magnificent animals were real, physical, living beings at one time. Instead of becoming extinct, the Unicorns raised their energy so that they are now spiritual beings.

Children and highly creative people naturally gravitate toward Unicorns because they can sense their pure, healing energy. In fact, inviting Unicorns into your life can help you to unleash your natural creativity.

To take you to the magical world of the unicorns and help you connect deeply with their energy, I've created a guided meditation and also a selection of enchanting, high-vibrational music to help quiet your mind as you colour. You'll find details of how to access this bonus content at the back of the book.

I highly recommend using nontoxic and fair trade colouring pencils, as the Unicorns care deeply about healing and preserving the environment. Let your imagination go wild with the colours you use. After all, Unicorns are associated with all the bright and sparkly colours of the rainbow!

Each message that accompanies the illustrations is a genuine message from the spirit of the Unicorns, because they wish to connect with and help you in any way they can.

Love, Doreen

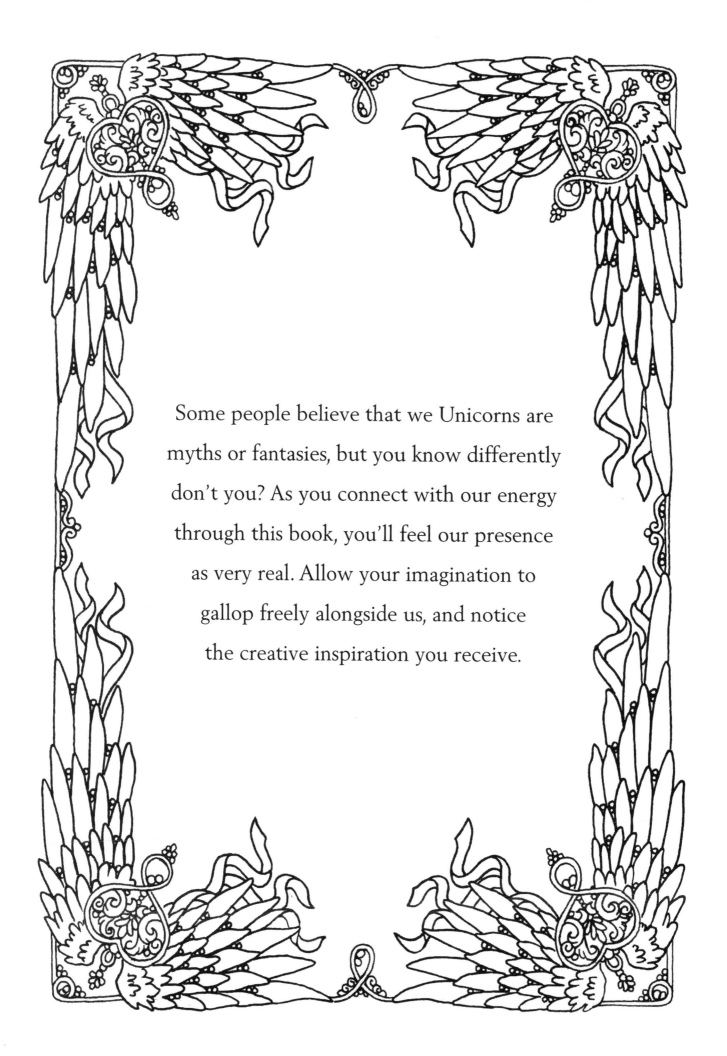

Some people believe that we Unicorns are myths or fantasies, but you know differently don't you? As you connect with our energy through this book, you'll feel our presence as very real. Allow your imagination to gallop freely alongside us, and notice the creative inspiration you receive.

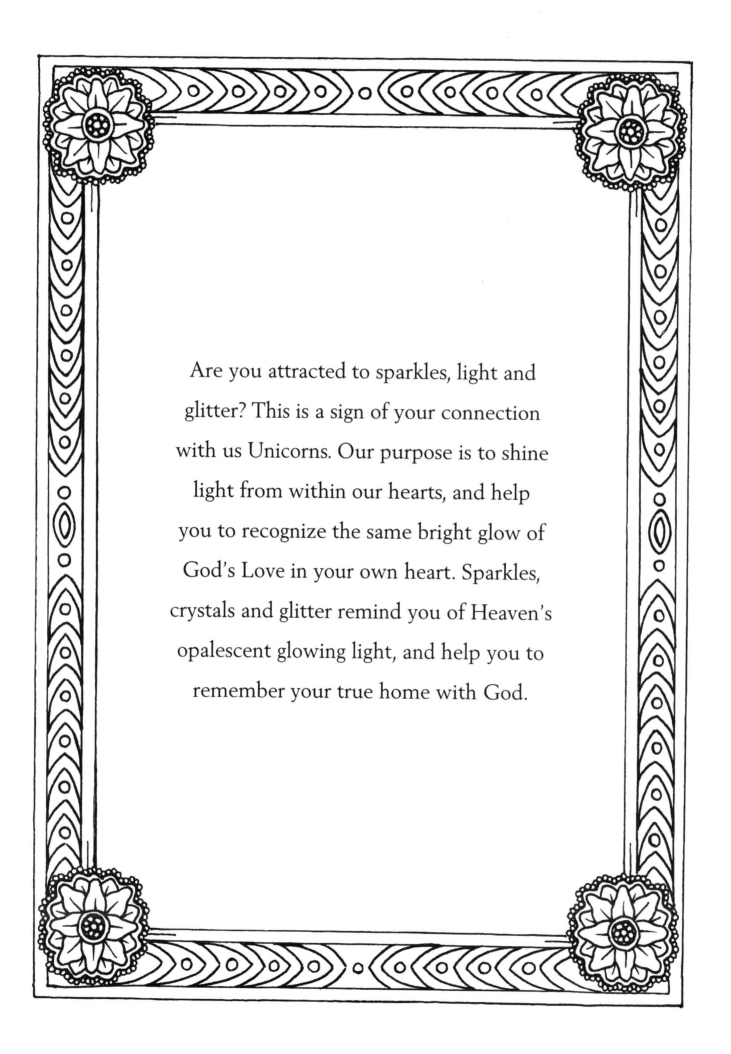

Are you attracted to sparkles, light and
glitter? This is a sign of your connection
with us Unicorns. Our purpose is to shine
light from within our hearts, and help
you to recognize the same bright glow of
God's Love in your own heart. Sparkles,
crystals and glitter remind you of Heaven's
opalescent glowing light, and help you to
remember your true home with God.

The reason you are attracted to us Unicorns is because the purity within you recognizes the purity within us. By connecting with our energy, you detoxify any negativity you may have absorbed. Call upon our Unicorn energy as you colour these pages, to lift away heavy energy, so that you can feel light and free as we do.

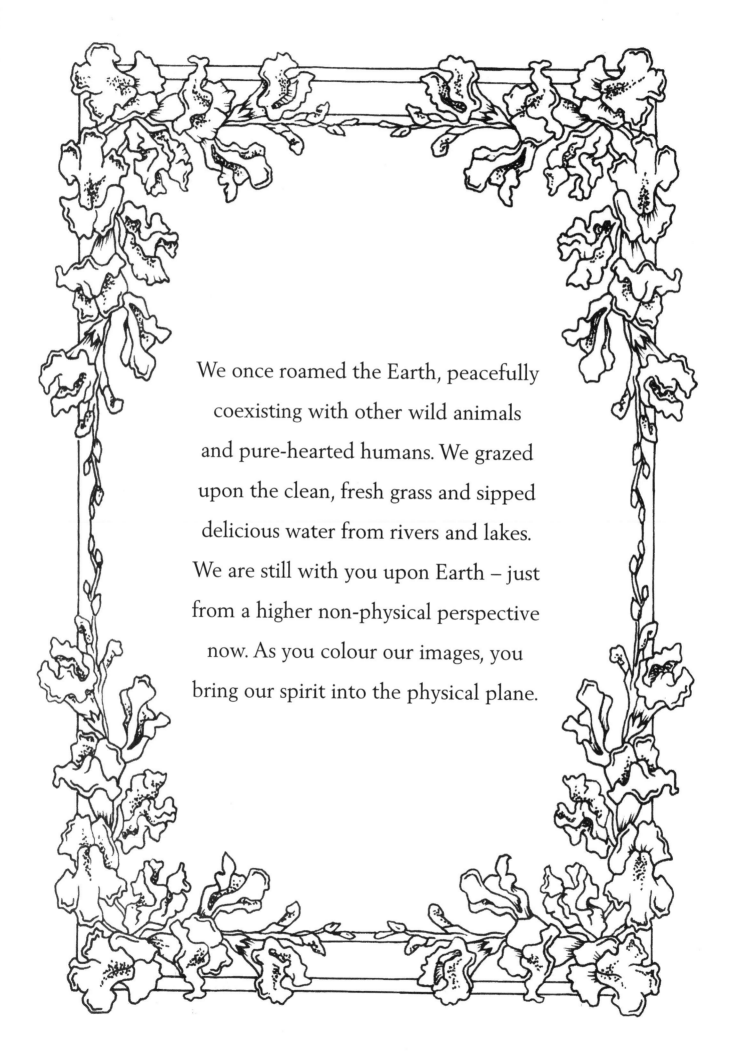

We once roamed the Earth, peacefully coexisting with other wild animals and pure-hearted humans. We grazed upon the clean, fresh grass and sipped delicious water from rivers and lakes. We are still with you upon Earth – just from a higher non-physical perspective now. As you colour our images, you bring our spirit into the physical plane.

Yes, it is true that we are wish-granters.
We love to grant wishes, and bring
happiness and joy wherever we go …
and we appreciate your gratitude for the
blessings bestowed upon you. Why not
make a wish right now, as you are colouring
this page? The colours will amplify your
positive visions and openness to receiving.

Like you, we Unicorns are highly sensitive.
We feel our emotions deeply, and we
can sense the energy of everyone we
meet. Sometimes, being sensitive can feel
overwhelming. To shield yourself you can
do what we Unicorns do: imagine a blanket
of rainbow energy surrounding you. Only
love can travel into and out of this blanket.

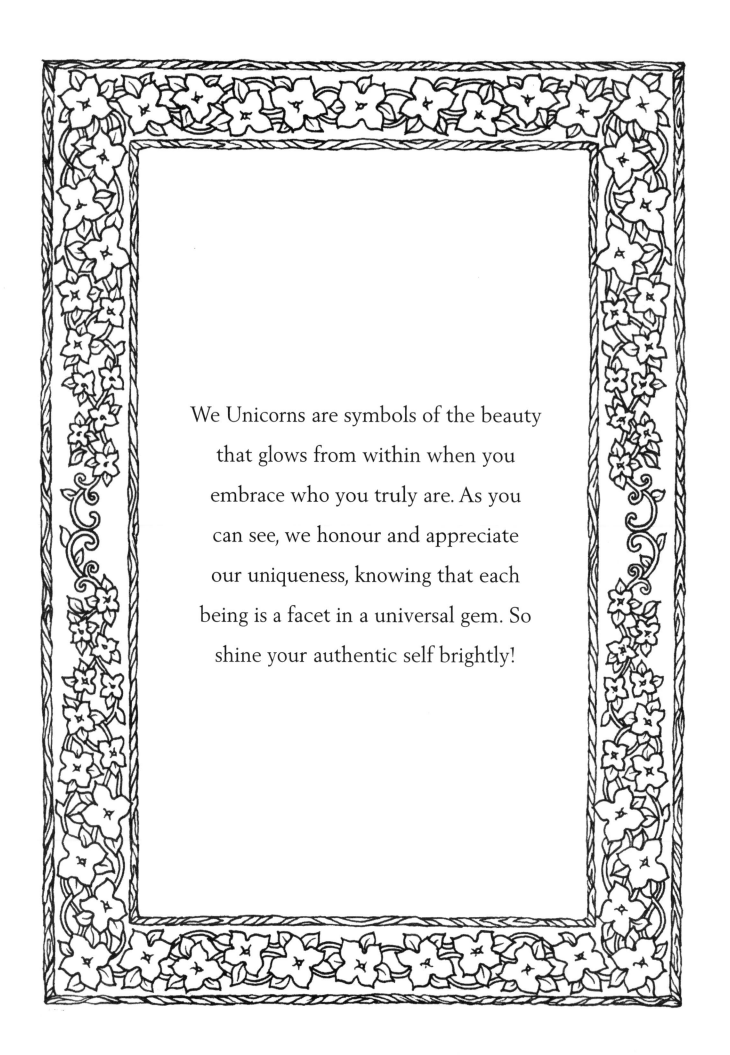

We Unicorns are symbols of the beauty that glows from within when you embrace who you truly are. As you can see, we honour and appreciate our uniqueness, knowing that each being is a facet in a universal gem. So shine your authentic self brightly!

We Unicorns stay in families and herds,
because we love one another and we enjoy
the deep bond we all share. Just like us, you
have a herd or family consisting of those to
whom you're related, and your 'family of
choice' beloved friends. Stay close to your
herd for comfort, safety and shared love.

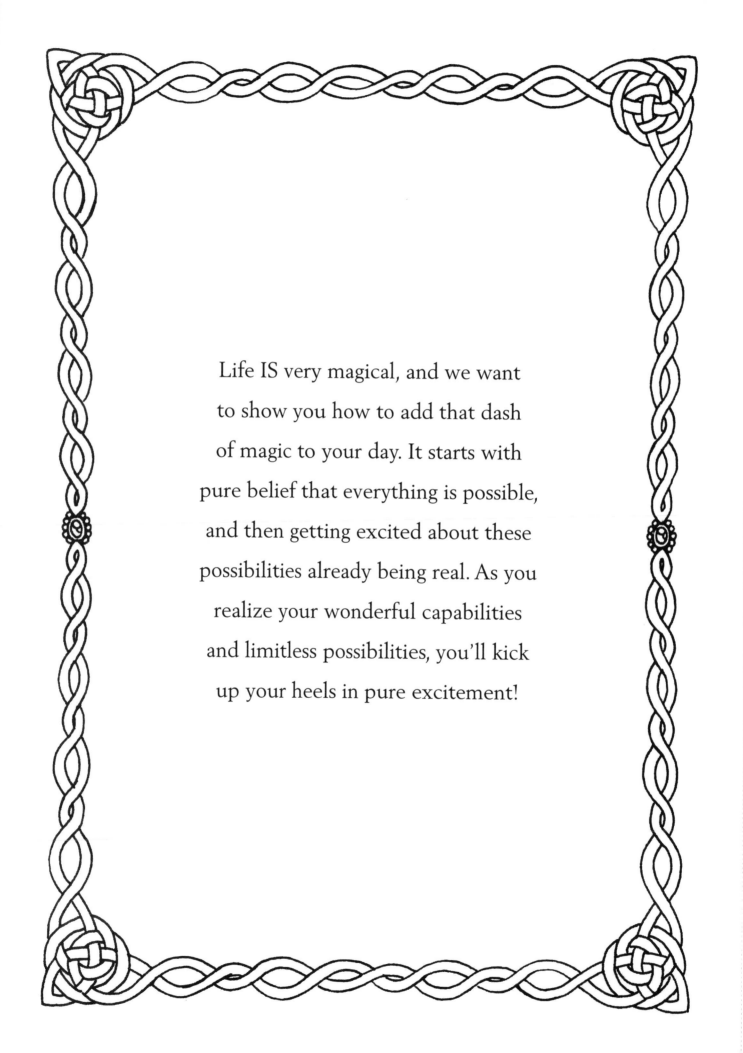

Life IS very magical, and we want
to show you how to add that dash
of magic to your day. It starts with
pure belief that everything is possible,
and then getting excited about these
possibilities already being real. As you
realize your wonderful capabilities
and limitless possibilities, you'll kick
up your heels in pure excitement!

We are here to bring dazzling rainbow colours to you. We don't understand why people would choose to dress and live in colourless ways, when so many vibrant hues and tones are available. As you look at each colour, notice how its vibrations uplift you. Please be colourful like us!

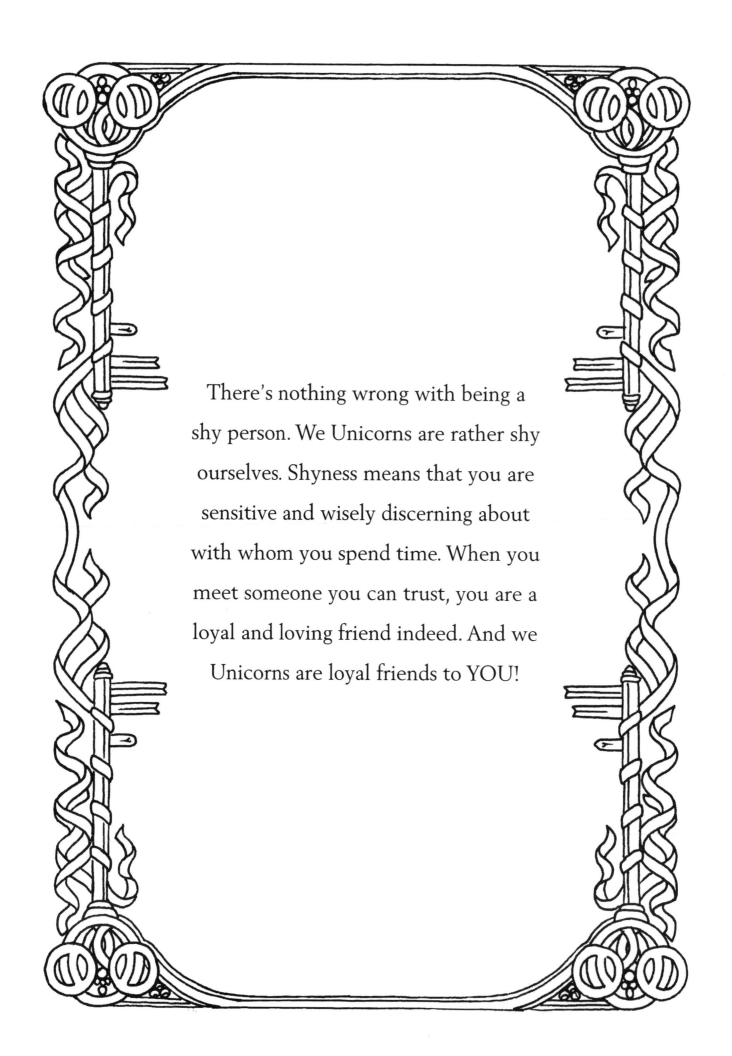

There's nothing wrong with being a shy person. We Unicorns are rather shy ourselves. Shyness means that you are sensitive and wisely discerning about with whom you spend time. When you meet someone you can trust, you are a loyal and loving friend indeed. And we Unicorns are loyal friends to YOU!

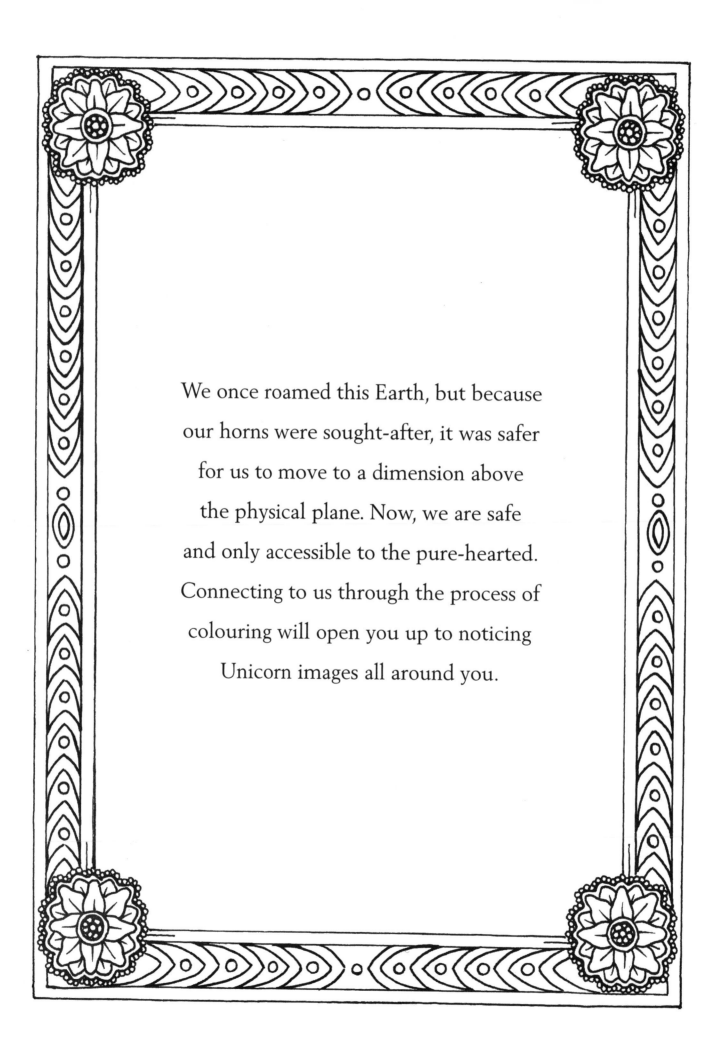

We once roamed this Earth, but because
our horns were sought-after, it was safer
for us to move to a dimension above
the physical plane. Now, we are safe
and only accessible to the pure-hearted.
Connecting to us through the process of
colouring will open you up to noticing
Unicorn images all around you.

As you engage with us through colouring these pages, please notice all of the creative ideas you receive, and put them into action. Your soul is calling you to express yourself creatively, for your health, happiness and purpose. Each creative idea is an answer to a prayer, giving you a pathway to be yourself fully, unafraid to be original and unique.

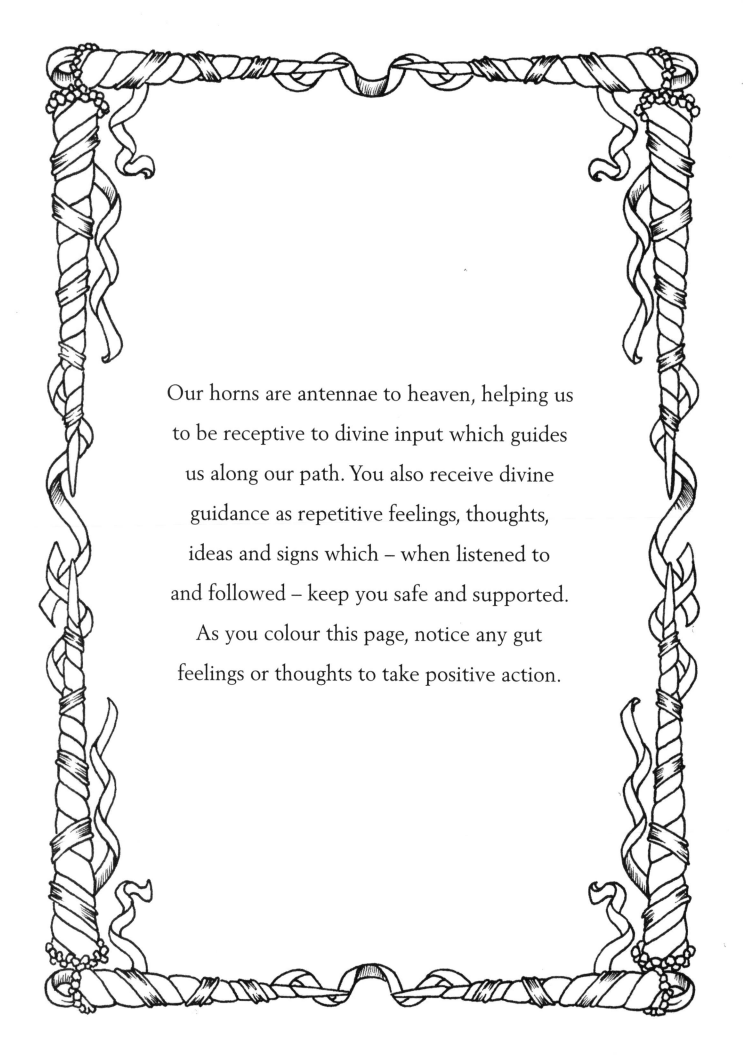

Our horns are antennae to heaven, helping us
to be receptive to divine input which guides
us along our path. You also receive divine
guidance as repetitive feelings, thoughts,
ideas and signs which – when listened to
and followed – keep you safe and supported.
As you colour this page, notice any gut
feelings or thoughts to take positive action.

I would love to take you on a journey to
an inner place filled with great beauty
and love. Please ride upon my back and
hold on while I lift you up to the fluffy
clouds and rainbows. We will leave all
Earthly concerns behind, and go to
a carefree place where there are no
sorrows or problems – a place that truly
exists within your heart right now.

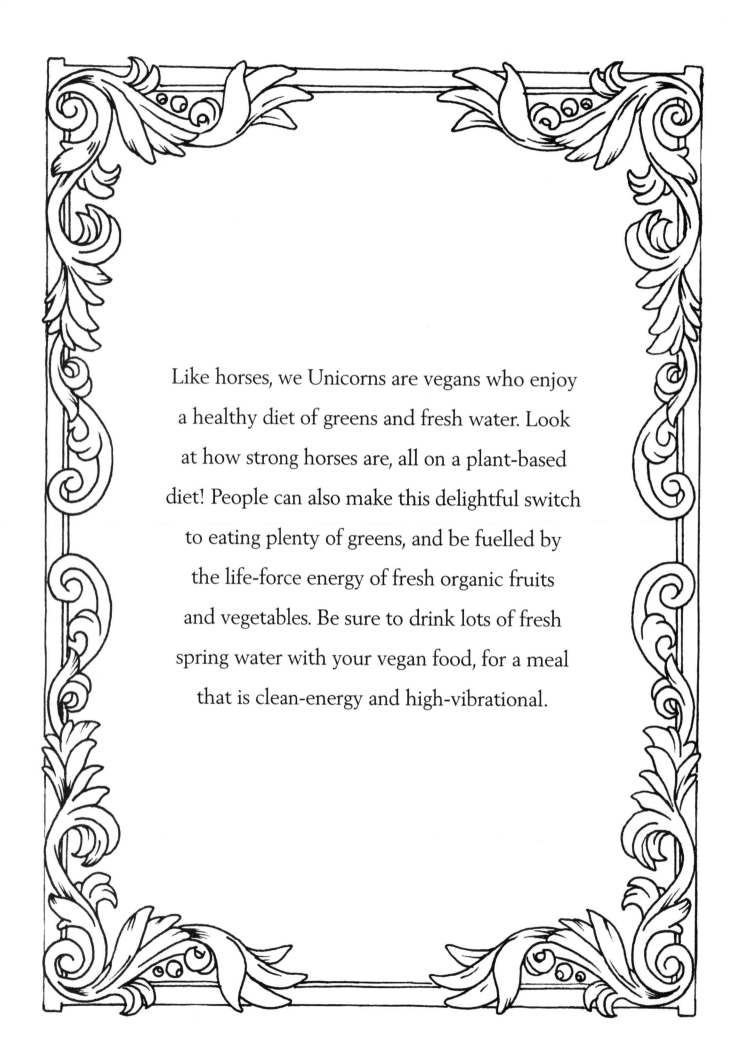

Like horses, we Unicorns are vegans who enjoy a healthy diet of greens and fresh water. Look at how strong horses are, all on a plant-based diet! People can also make this delightful switch to eating plenty of greens, and be fuelled by the life-force energy of fresh organic fruits and vegetables. Be sure to drink lots of fresh spring water with your vegan food, for a meal that is clean-energy and high-vibrational.

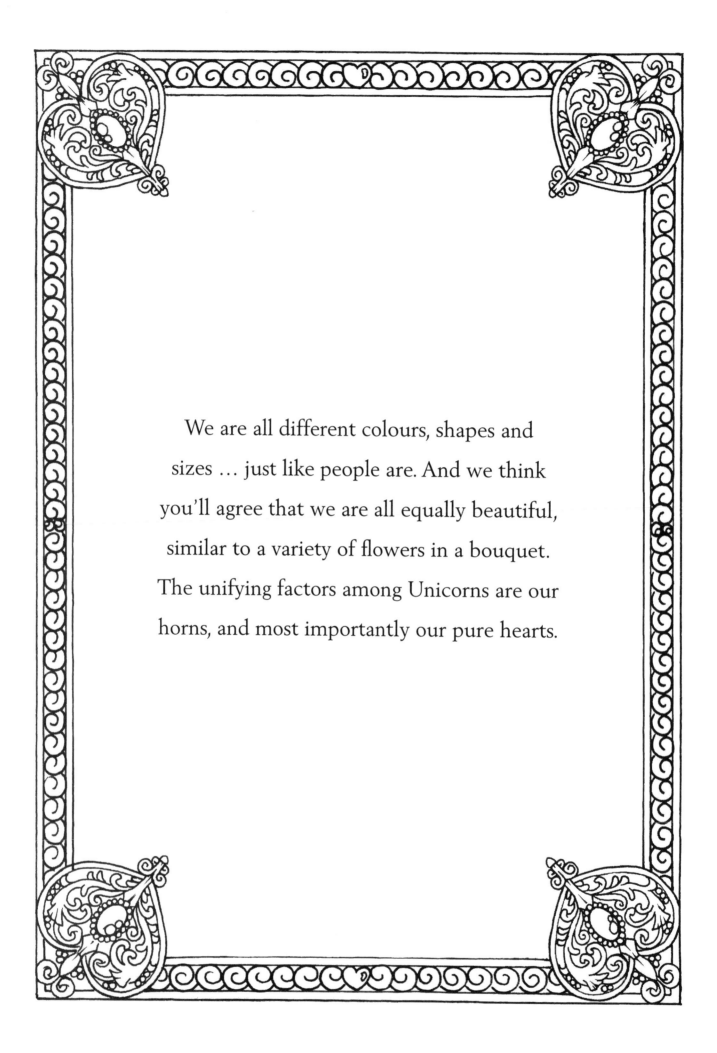

We are all different colours, shapes and sizes … just like people are. And we think you'll agree that we are all equally beautiful, similar to a variety of flowers in a bouquet. The unifying factors among Unicorns are our horns, and most importantly our pure hearts.

What do you dream of? There's an alternative reality that we can enter together, where dreams are born in beautiful, bold colours. This rainbow-coloured path is filled with happy, joyful feelings. Together, we can kick up our heels in delight at the endless possibilities awaiting us!

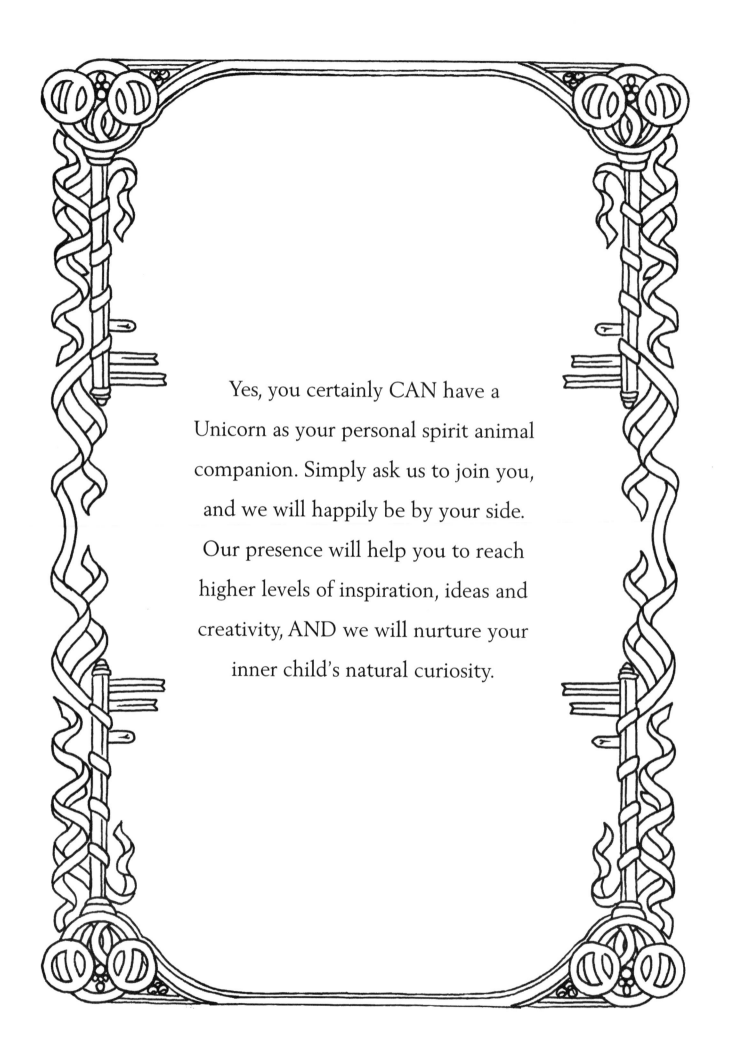

Yes, you certainly CAN have a
Unicorn as your personal spirit animal
companion. Simply ask us to join you,
and we will happily be by your side.
Our presence will help you to reach
higher levels of inspiration, ideas and
creativity, AND we will nurture your
inner child's natural curiosity.

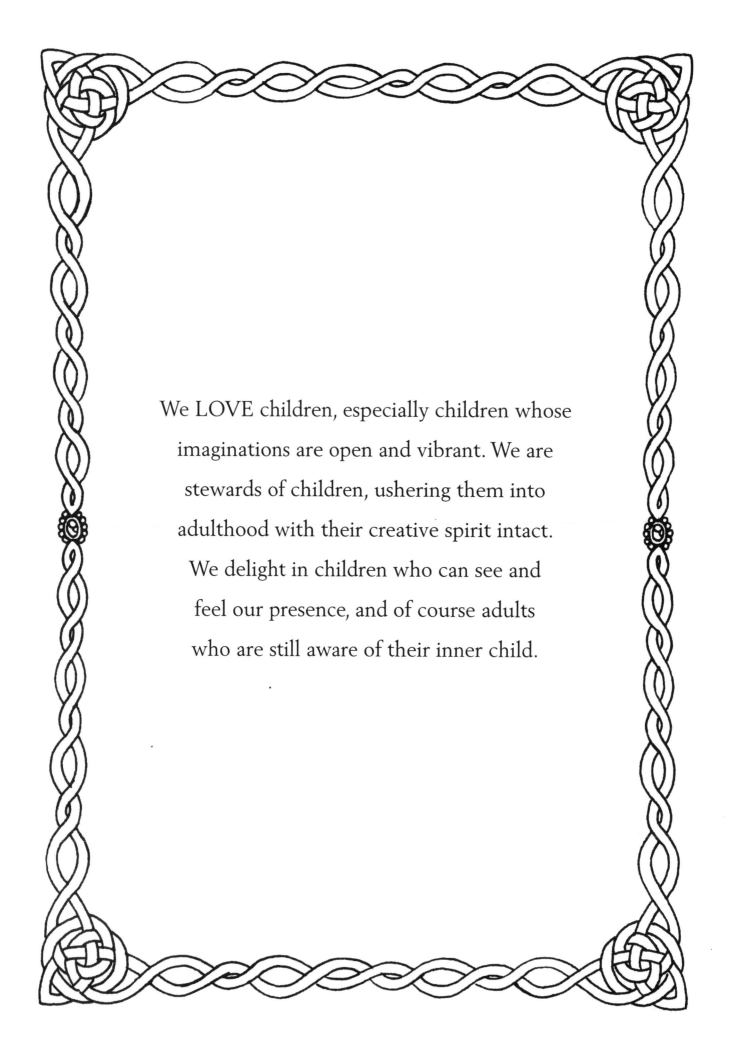

We LOVE children, especially children whose
imaginations are open and vibrant. We are
stewards of children, ushering them into
adulthood with their creative spirit intact.
We delight in children who can see and
feel our presence, and of course adults
who are still aware of their inner child.

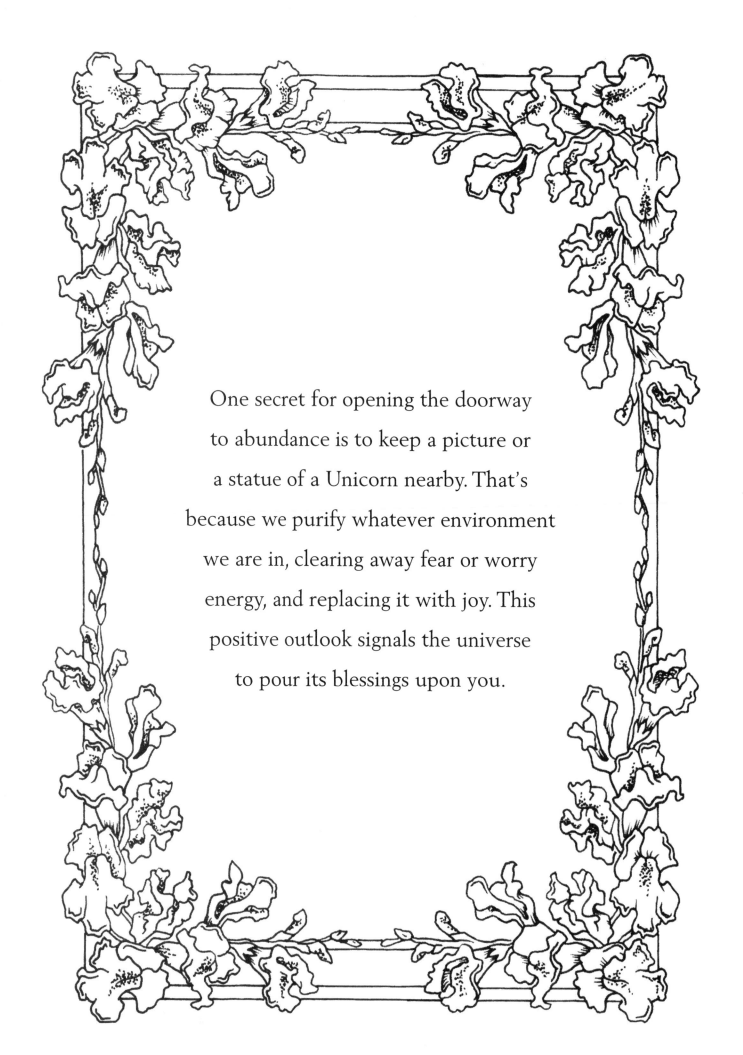

One secret for opening the doorway
to abundance is to keep a picture or
a statue of a Unicorn nearby. That's
because we purify whatever environment
we are in, clearing away fear or worry
energy, and replacing it with joy. This
positive outlook signals the universe
to pour its blessings upon you.

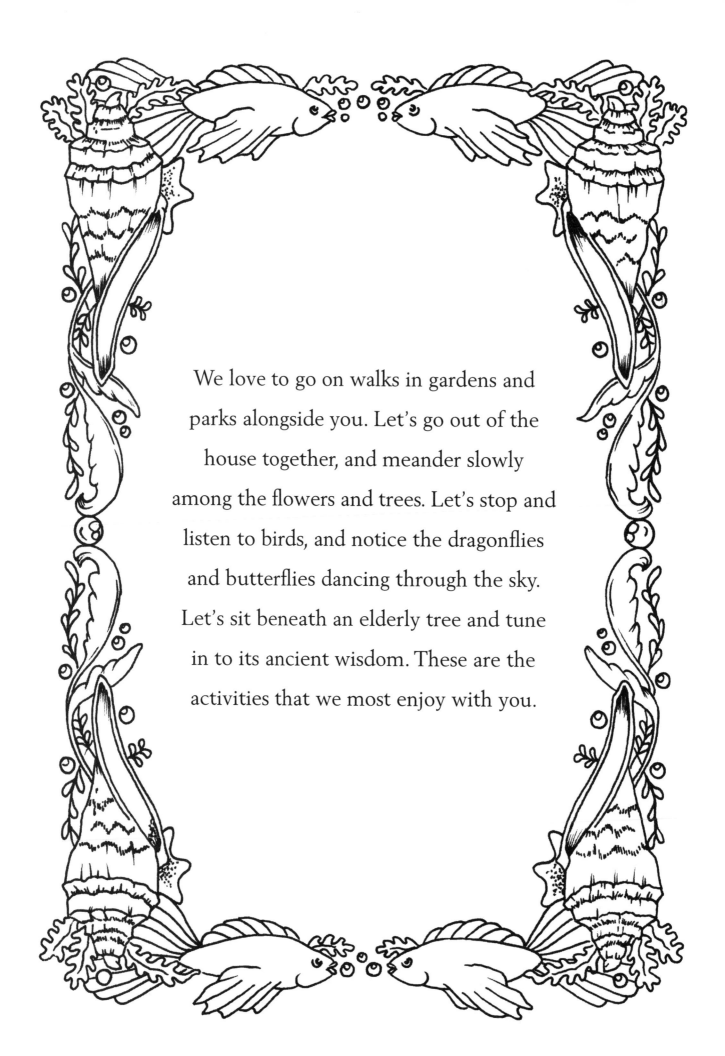

We love to go on walks in gardens and parks alongside you. Let's go out of the house together, and meander slowly among the flowers and trees. Let's stop and listen to birds, and notice the dragonflies and butterflies dancing through the sky. Let's sit beneath an elderly tree and tune in to its ancient wisdom. These are the activities that we most enjoy with you.

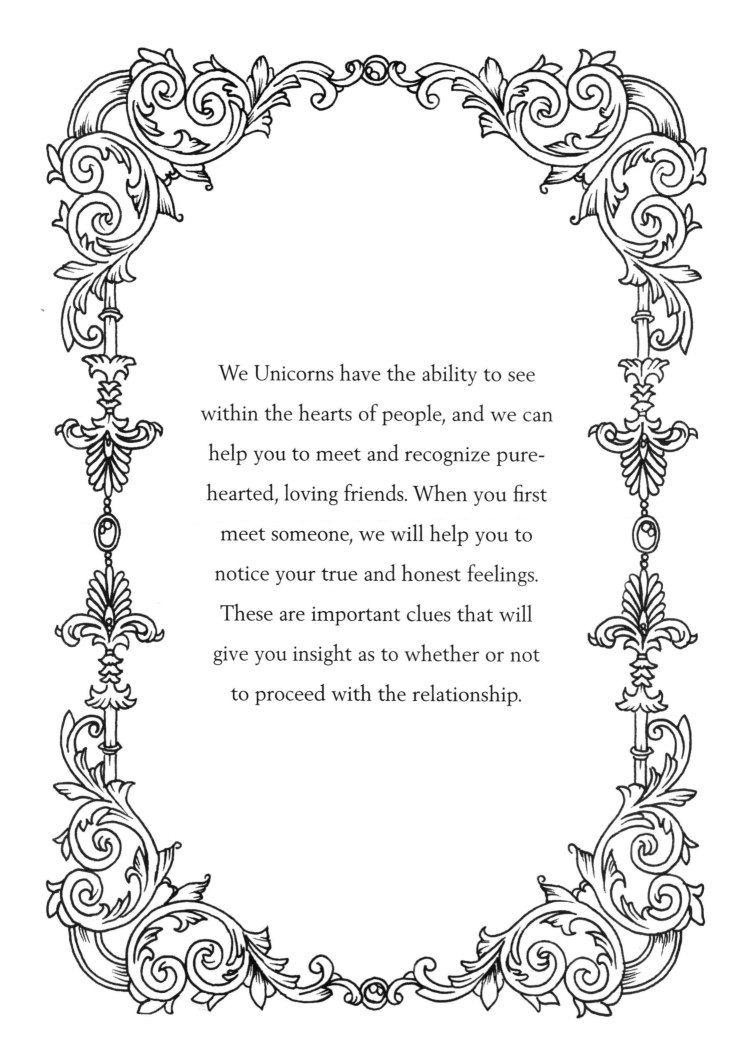

We Unicorns have the ability to see within the hearts of people, and we can help you to meet and recognize pure-hearted, loving friends. When you first meet someone, we will help you to notice your true and honest feelings. These are important clues that will give you insight as to whether or not to proceed with the relationship.

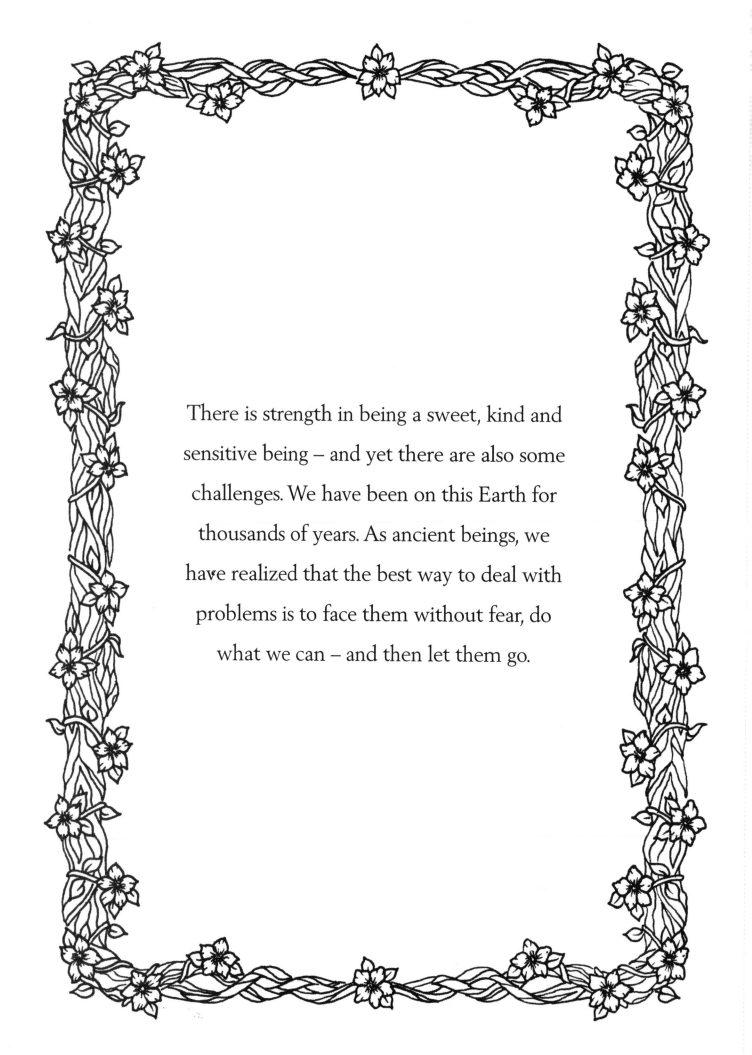

There is strength in being a sweet, kind and sensitive being – and yet there are also some challenges. We have been on this Earth for thousands of years. As ancient beings, we have realized that the best way to deal with problems is to face them without fear, do what we can – and then let them go.

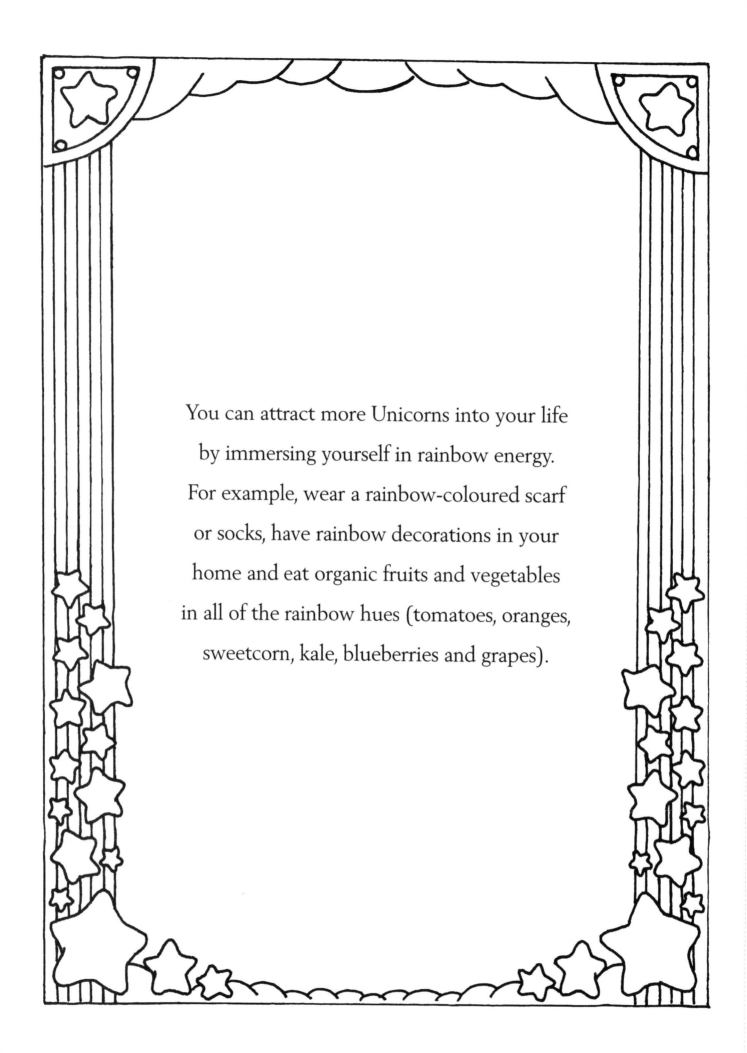

You can attract more Unicorns into your life by immersing yourself in rainbow energy. For example, wear a rainbow-coloured scarf or socks, have rainbow decorations in your home and eat organic fruits and vegetables in all of the rainbow hues (tomatoes, oranges, sweetcorn, kale, blueberries and grapes).

We are so much more than horses with horns upon our heads! We have worked diligently to become the highest vibrational and purest examples of beings who have their hearts completely open to compassion and unconditional love. Being in our presence by colouring these images, and surrounding yourself with images of Unicorns, automatically uplifts your outlook and opens your heart.

Although we are part of a herd just like you, sometimes it's important to retreat by yourself. We Unicorns know the importance of soaking in water as a way of clearing and hearing our inner thoughts. As you colour this page, focus upon your own inner thoughts. Or even better, take a nice warm bath with flowers or essential oils for your own personal retreat.

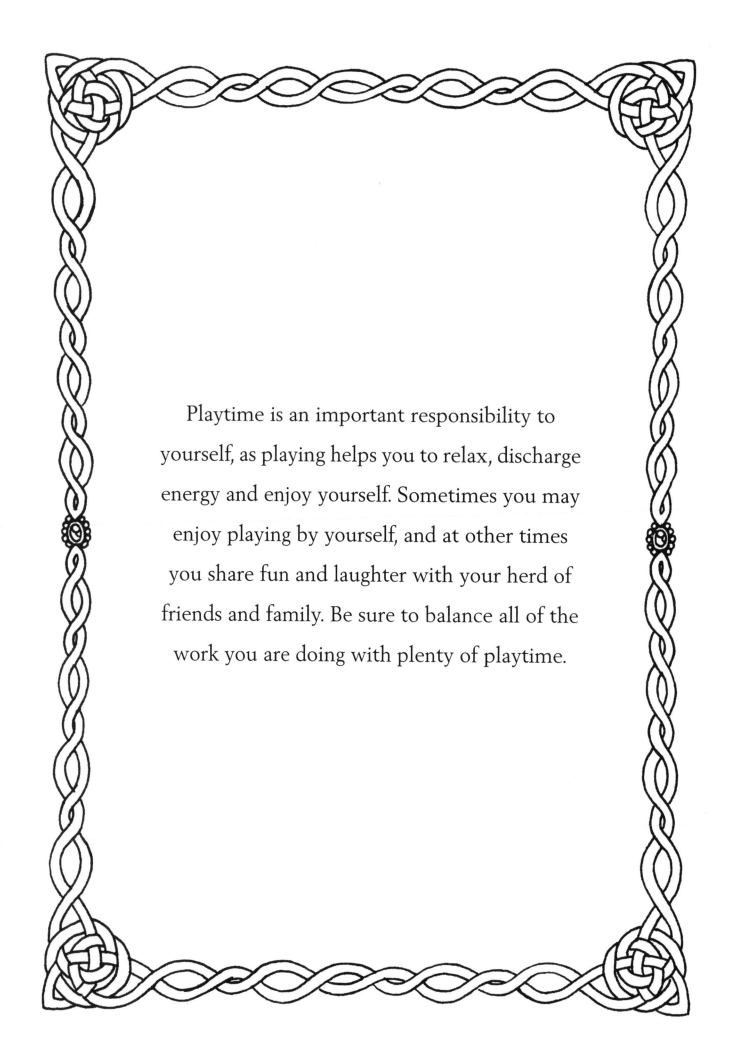

Playtime is an important responsibility to yourself, as playing helps you to relax, discharge energy and enjoy yourself. Sometimes you may enjoy playing by yourself, and at other times you share fun and laughter with your herd of friends and family. Be sure to balance all of the work you are doing with plenty of playtime.

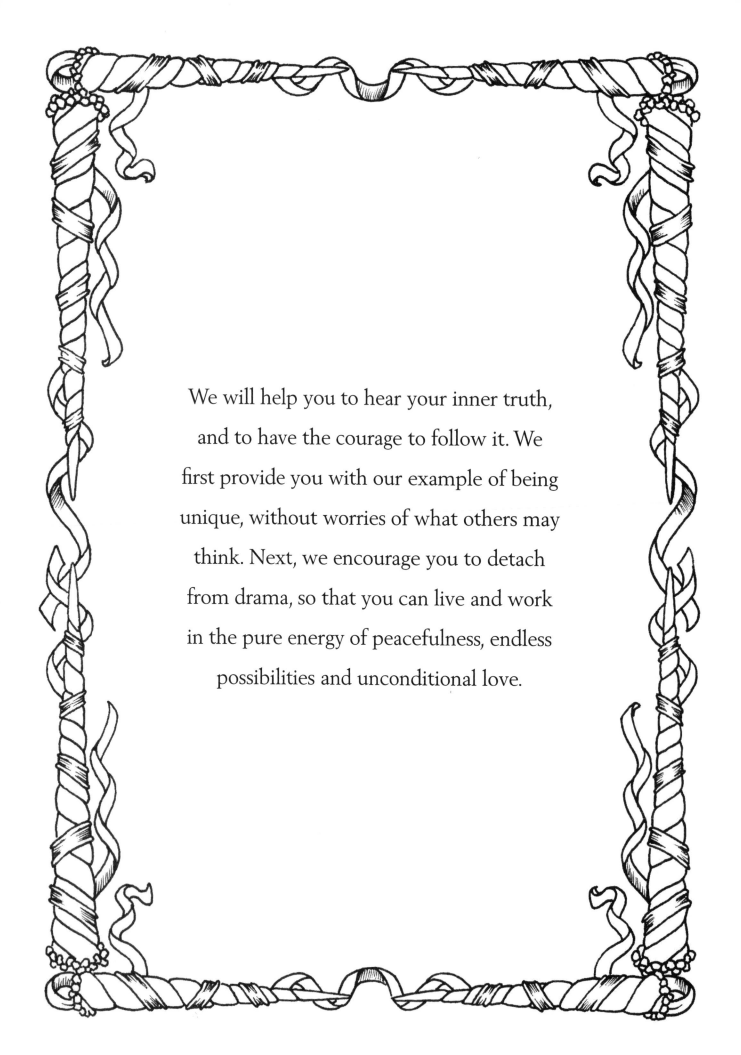

We will help you to hear your inner truth, and to have the courage to follow it. We first provide you with our example of being unique, without worries of what others may think. Next, we encourage you to detach from drama, so that you can live and work in the pure energy of peacefulness, endless possibilities and unconditional love.

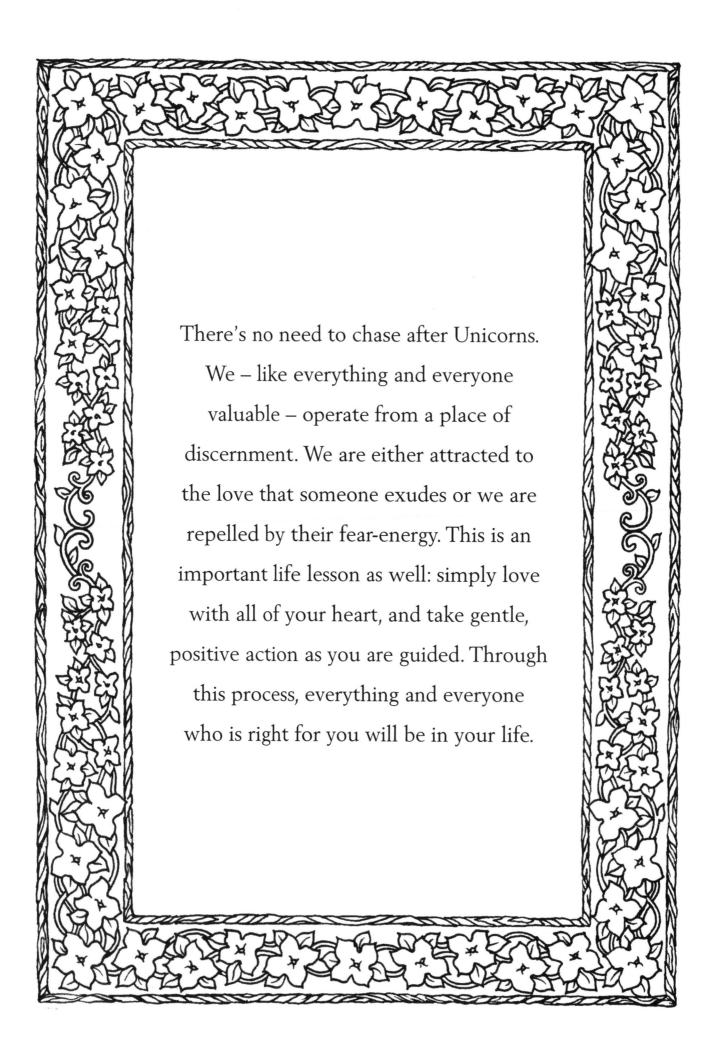

There's no need to chase after Unicorns. We – like everything and everyone valuable – operate from a place of discernment. We are either attracted to the love that someone exudes or we are repelled by their fear-energy. This is an important life lesson as well: simply love with all of your heart, and take gentle, positive action as you are guided. Through this process, everything and everyone who is right for you will be in your life.

We love our freedom, which allows us to gallop and fly freely. We'd love to help you to enjoy greater freedom as well. Most restrictions and limits are in the mind, where you believe someone else has more rights than you. They don't! You have the right to happiness and freedom, and you can take back your power right now if you choose.

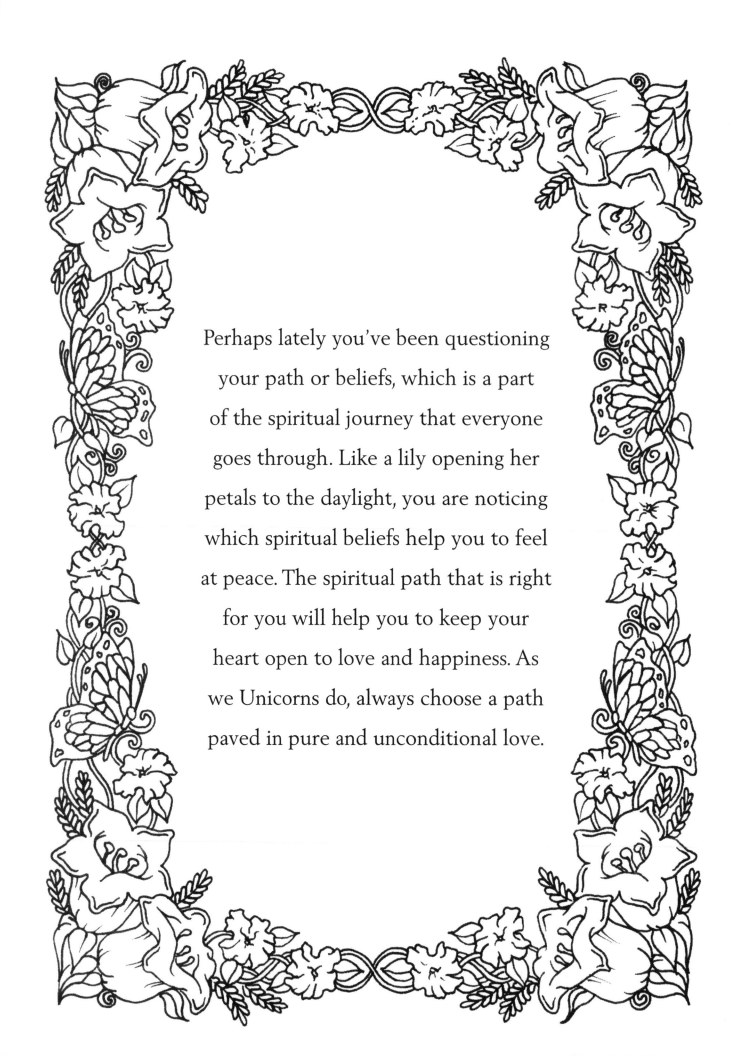

Perhaps lately you've been questioning
your path or beliefs, which is a part
of the spiritual journey that everyone
goes through. Like a lily opening her
petals to the daylight, you are noticing
which spiritual beliefs help you to feel
at peace. The spiritual path that is right
for you will help you to keep your
heart open to love and happiness. As
we Unicorns do, always choose a path
paved in pure and unconditional love.

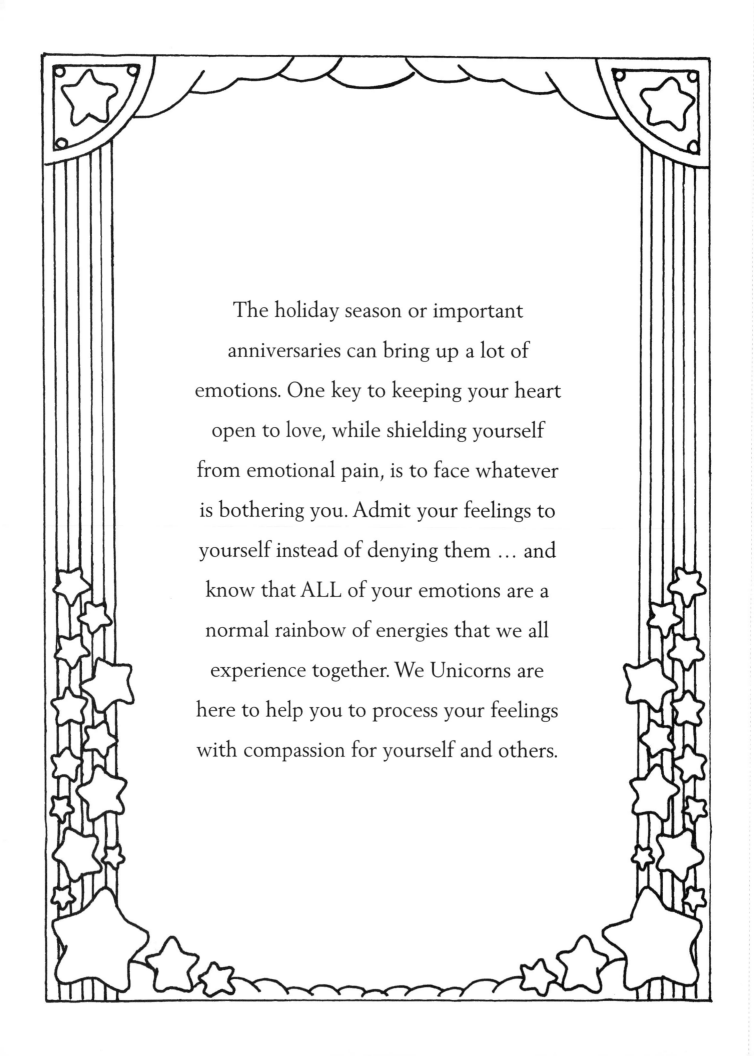

The holiday season or important anniversaries can bring up a lot of emotions. One key to keeping your heart open to love, while shielding yourself from emotional pain, is to face whatever is bothering you. Admit your feelings to yourself instead of denying them … and know that ALL of your emotions are a normal rainbow of energies that we all experience together. We Unicorns are here to help you to process your feelings with compassion for yourself and others.

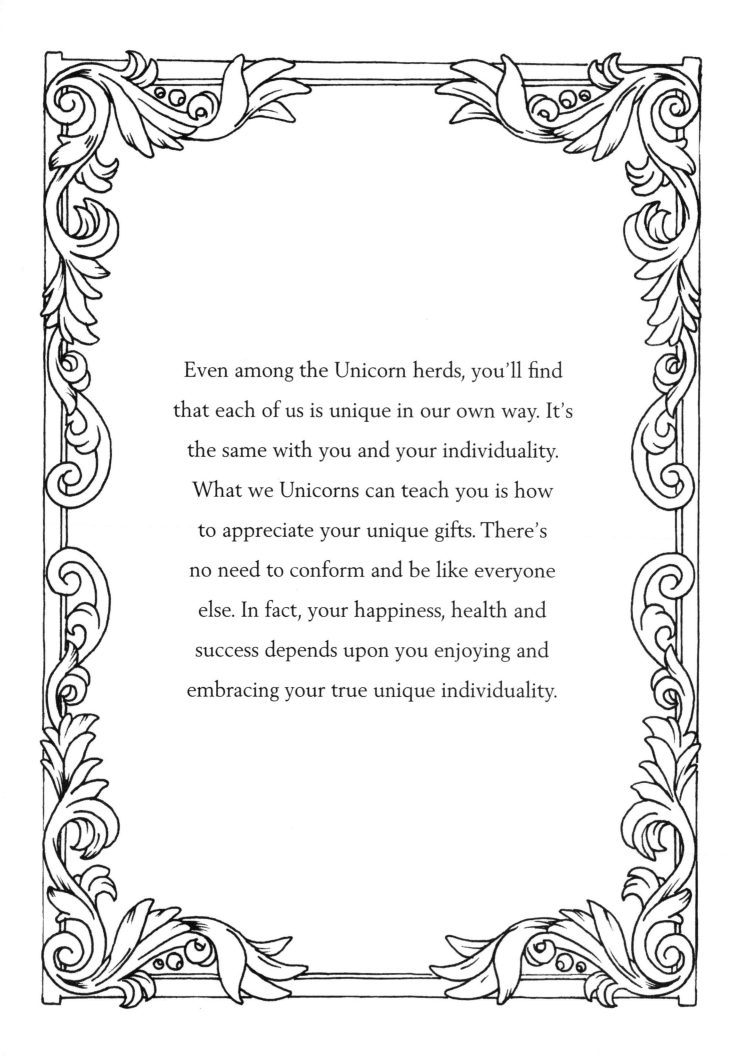

Even among the Unicorn herds, you'll find
that each of us is unique in our own way. It's
the same with you and your individuality.
What we Unicorns can teach you is how
to appreciate your unique gifts. There's
no need to conform and be like everyone
else. In fact, your happiness, health and
success depends upon you enjoying and
embracing your true unique individuality.

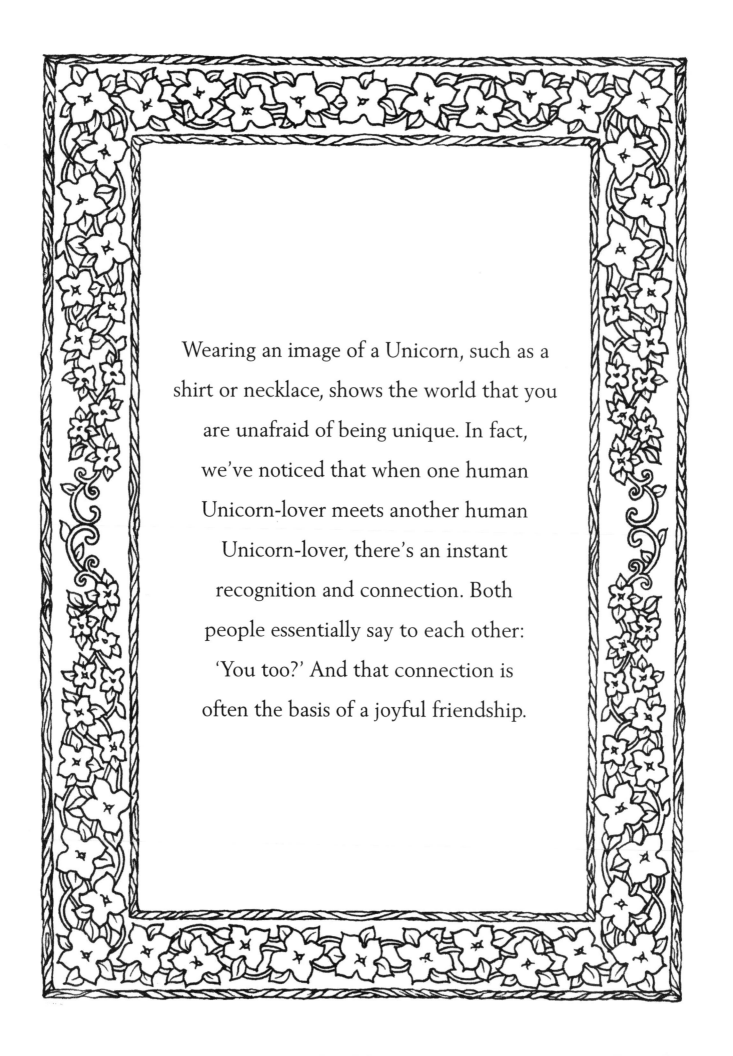

Wearing an image of a Unicorn, such as a shirt or necklace, shows the world that you are unafraid of being unique. In fact, we've noticed that when one human Unicorn-lover meets another human Unicorn-lover, there's an instant recognition and connection. Both people essentially say to each other: 'You too?' And that connection is often the basis of a joyful friendship.

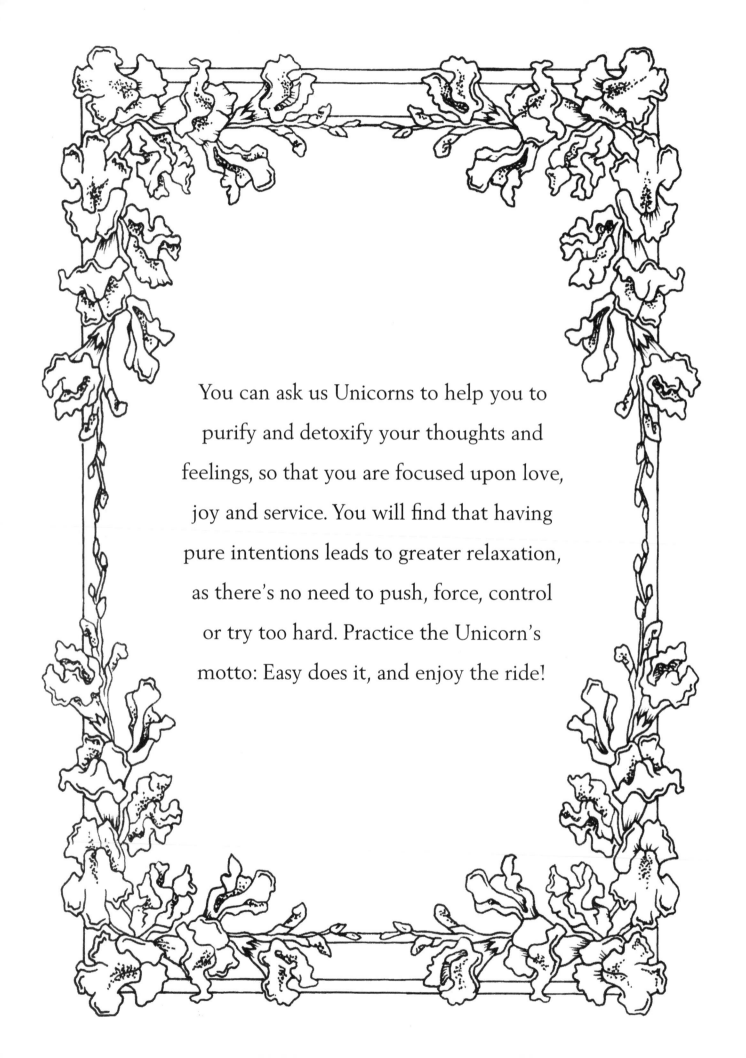

You can ask us Unicorns to help you to purify and detoxify your thoughts and feelings, so that you are focused upon love, joy and service. You will find that having pure intentions leads to greater relaxation, as there's no need to push, force, control or try too hard. Practice the Unicorn's motto: Easy does it, and enjoy the ride!

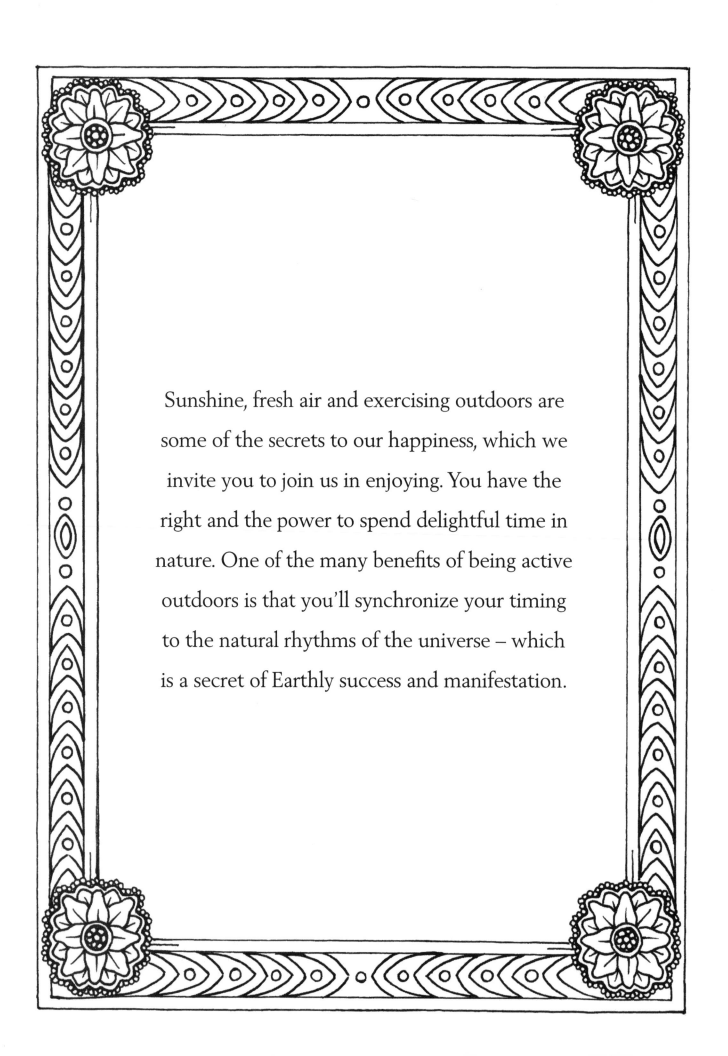

Sunshine, fresh air and exercising outdoors are some of the secrets to our happiness, which we invite you to join us in enjoying. You have the right and the power to spend delightful time in nature. One of the many benefits of being active outdoors is that you'll synchronize your timing to the natural rhythms of the universe – which is a secret of Earthly success and manifestation.

Your authentic natural self is divinely perfect! There's no need to mask – or try to change – your real self, as God created you as you're supposed to be for your life purpose. Let go of any insecurities about impressing others, as your true friends appreciate who you are. Yes, we can all learn and grow, including having compassion for yourself when you feel insecure or afraid.

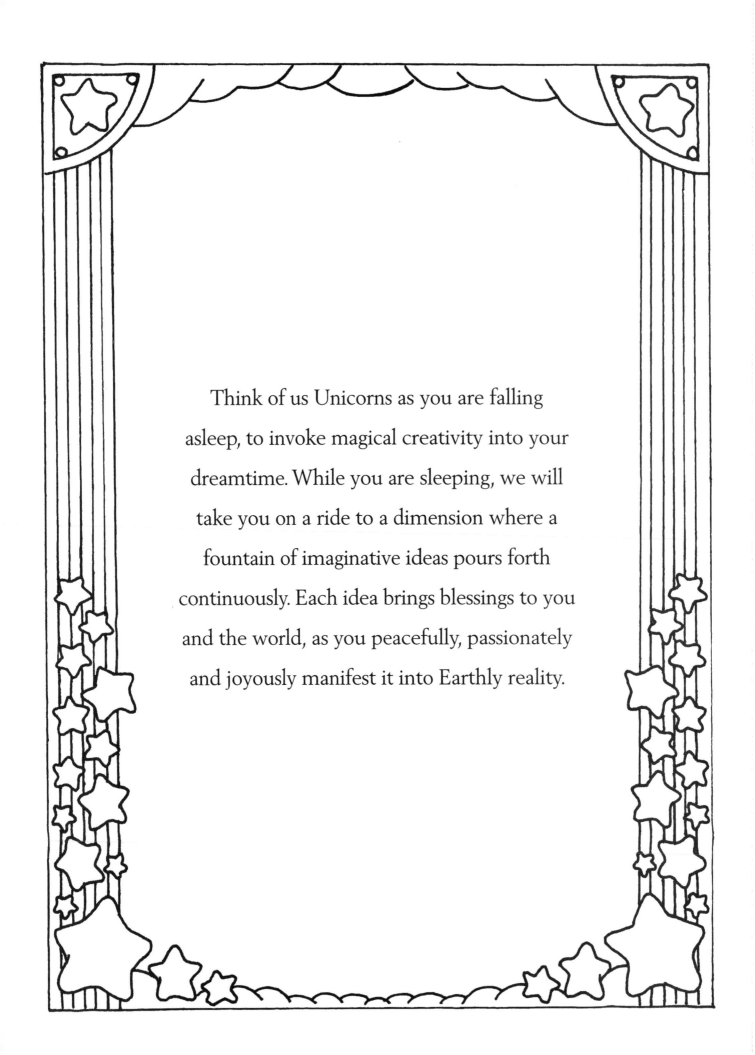

Think of us Unicorns as you are falling asleep, to invoke magical creativity into your dreamtime. While you are sleeping, we will take you on a ride to a dimension where a fountain of imaginative ideas pours forth continuously. Each idea brings blessings to you and the world, as you peacefully, passionately and joyously manifest it into Earthly reality.

We often wear flowers in our manes, and we encourage you to connect with flowers too. Flowers are earthly angels who selflessly give beauty, fragrance and pollen food. Growing flowers is the ultimate way to develop an intimate knowledge of the flowers' powerful healing energy. You can also connect through flower essences and spending time in flower gardens.

Our favourite music is that provided by nature: the sweet songs of the birds; the whistle of the wind; the rustle of blowing leaves; the call of wild animals and the sounds of the ocean. Listening to the music of nature necessarily quiets the mind and shuts out the noise. Make it a practice to spend time in nature, drinking in the tranquil sounds.

Just like you, we Unicorns give all glory to God for creating us from pure, unconditional love. The more we focus upon love, the more love we experience and receive. Each time that you or I accept and give love, we are honouring God's mission to create a world of peace, love, harmony … and rainbows!

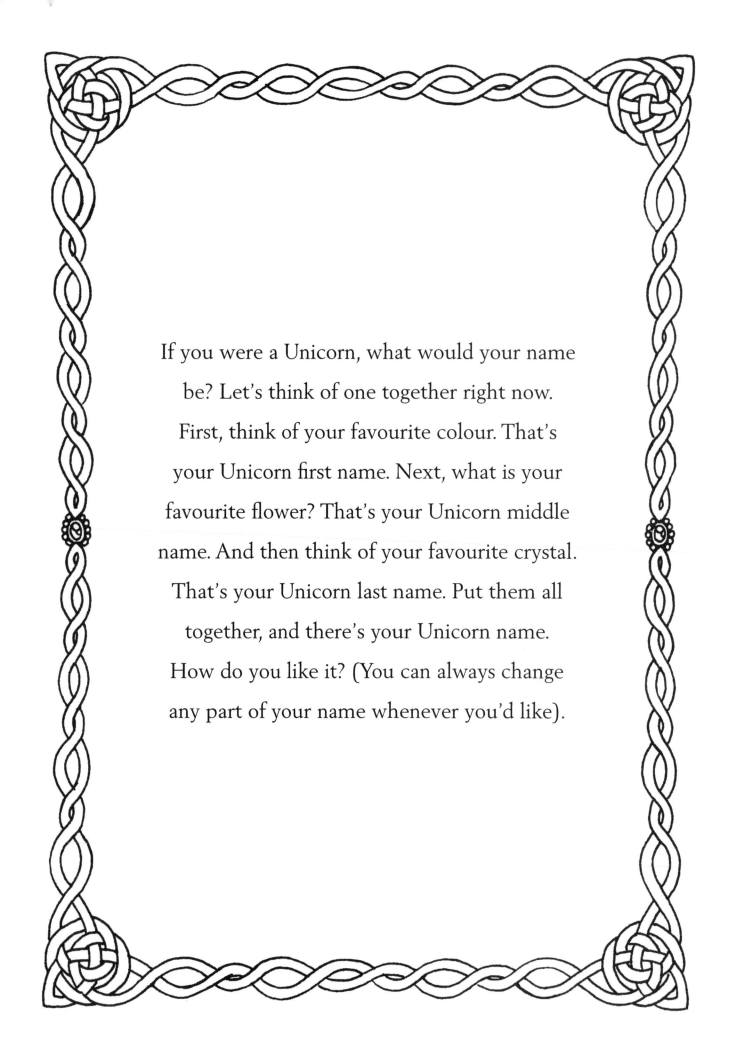

If you were a Unicorn, what would your name be? Let's think of one together right now. First, think of your favourite colour. That's your Unicorn first name. Next, what is your favourite flower? That's your Unicorn middle name. And then think of your favourite crystal. That's your Unicorn last name. Put them all together, and there's your Unicorn name. How do you like it? (You can always change any part of your name whenever you'd like).

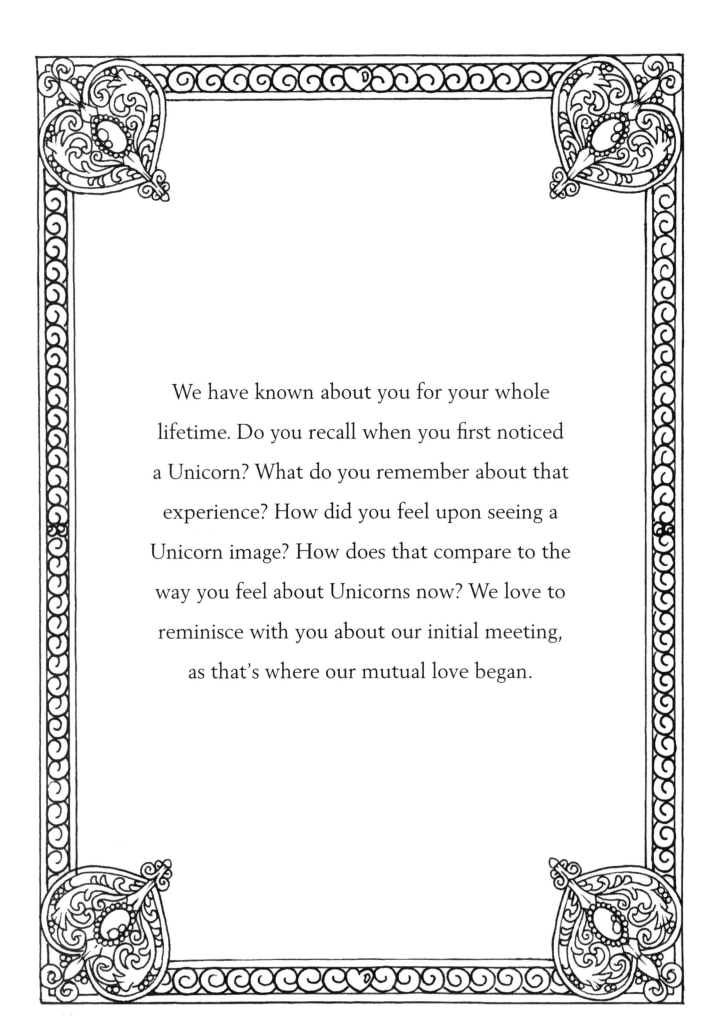

We have known about you for your whole lifetime. Do you recall when you first noticed a Unicorn? What do you remember about that experience? How did you feel upon seeing a Unicorn image? How does that compare to the way you feel about Unicorns now? We love to reminisce with you about our initial meeting, as that's where our mutual love began.

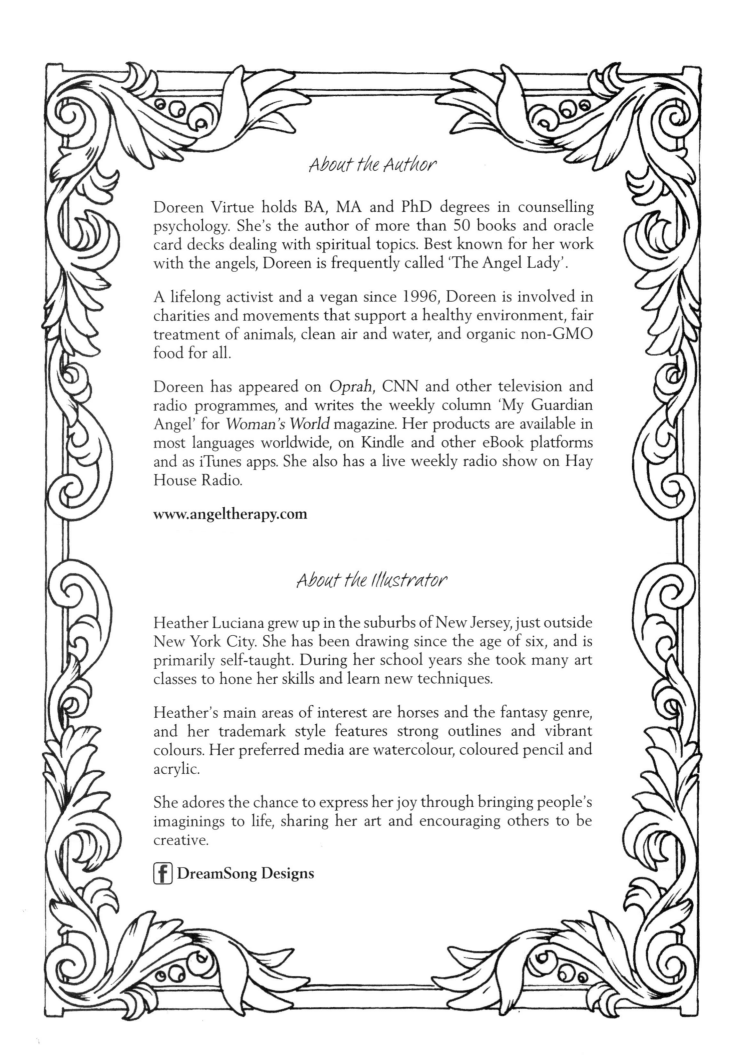

About the Author

Doreen Virtue holds BA, MA and PhD degrees in counselling psychology. She's the author of more than 50 books and oracle card decks dealing with spiritual topics. Best known for her work with the angels, Doreen is frequently called 'The Angel Lady'.

A lifelong activist and a vegan since 1996, Doreen is involved in charities and movements that support a healthy environment, fair treatment of animals, clean air and water, and organic non-GMO food for all.

Doreen has appeared on *Oprah*, CNN and other television and radio programmes, and writes the weekly column 'My Guardian Angel' for *Woman's World* magazine. Her products are available in most languages worldwide, on Kindle and other eBook platforms and as iTunes apps. She also has a live weekly radio show on Hay House Radio.

www.angeltherapy.com

About the Illustrator

Heather Luciana grew up in the suburbs of New Jersey, just outside New York City. She has been drawing since the age of six, and is primarily self-taught. During her school years she took many art classes to hone her skills and learn new techniques.

Heather's main areas of interest are horses and the fantasy genre, and her trademark style features strong outlines and vibrant colours. Her preferred media are watercolour, coloured pencil and acrylic.

She adores the chance to express her joy through bringing people's imaginings to life, sharing her art and encouraging others to be creative.

DreamSong Designs

Bonus Content

Thank you for purchasing *Messages from the Unicorns Colouring Book* by Doreen Virtue. This product includes a free download! To access this bonus content, please visit www.hayhouse.com/download and enter the Product ID and Download Code as they appear below:

Product ID: 5289

Download Code: unicorn

For further assistance, please contact Hay House Customer Care by phone: US (800) 654-5126 or INTL CC+(760) 431-7695 or visit www.hayhouse.com/contact.

Thank you again for your Hay House purchase. Enjoy!

Hay House, Inc. • P.O. Box 5100 • Carlsbad, CA 92018 • (800) 654-5126

Caution: This audio program features meditation/visualization exercises that render it inappropriate for use while driving or operating heavy machinery.

Publisher's note: Hay House products are intended to be powerful, inspirational, and life-changing tools for personal growth and healing. They are not intended as a substitute for medical care. Please use this audio program under the supervision of your care provider. Neither the author nor Hay House, Inc., assumes any responsibility for your improper use of this product.

Hay House Colouring Books

9781781807453
£9.99

9781781807460
£9.99

9781781808320
£9.99

9781781806456
£9.99

9781781807880
£9.99

9781781806463
£9.99